LAMAR
Makes Pancakes

by Auntie Sierra

Enjoy more books by Auntie Sierra

  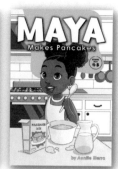 

Visit AuntieSierra.com

Written By Auntie Sierra
Illustrated by David Ampudia Martinez

ISBN 979-8-9857022-5-5

Siohan Press
www.siohanpress.com

Today is the day that Lamar
makes pancakes.

Lamar loves to cook.

He goes to the kitchen to get started.

Lamar gets the bowl. "I need a spoon," Lamar says.

Lamar puts the pancake mix in the bowl.

He adds water to the pancake mix.

He stirs and stirs. The mix is getting smooth.

What shape will he make the pancakes?

Lamar gets the cookie cutters.

The cookie cutters have many shapes.

This one looks like a star.

This one looks like a tree.

15

Lamar gets help to spray the griddle with oil.

16

He puts the star on the griddle.

He pours the pancake mix into the star.

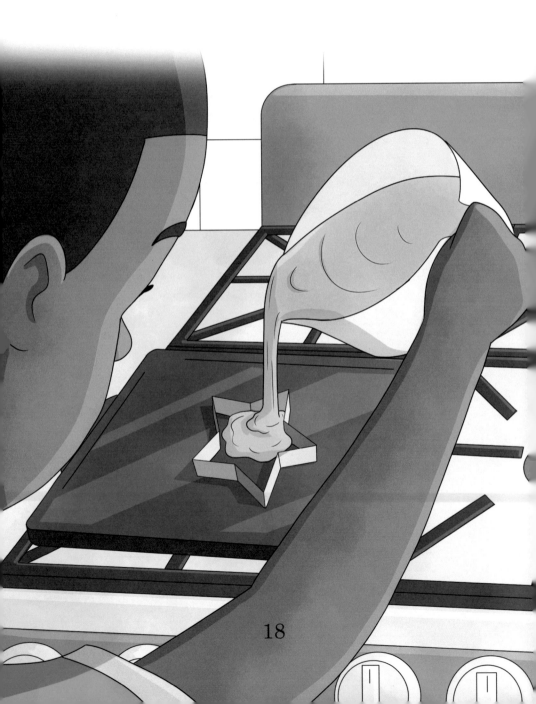

The pancake starts to bubble.

Lamar flips the pancake over.

"Looks like it is done," says Lamar.

He gets help to get the pancake
off of the griddle.

"Let's make sure it is cool before we take the pancake out of the cookie cutter," he says.

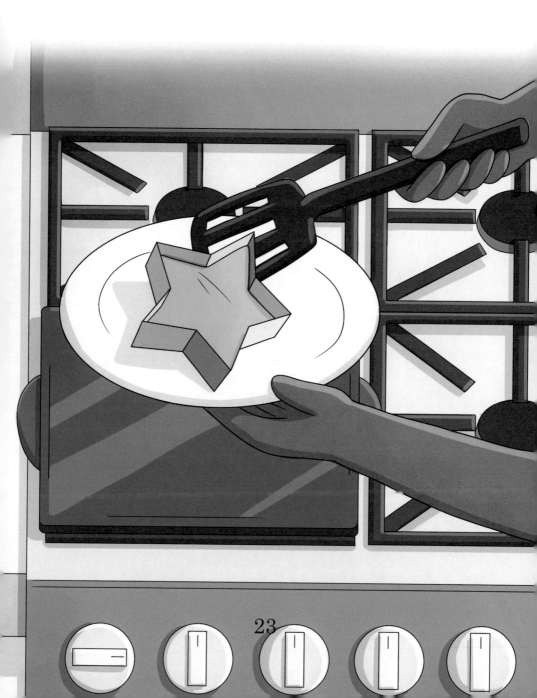

Lamar removes the pancake from the cookie cutter.

"I did it! I made a star pancake!"
he says.

25

He makes two more pancakes.

One pancake is a tree. One pancake is a star.

How many pancakes does Lamar have now?

He gets the syrup and
blueberries.

"Breakfast is ready," says Lamar.

"This looks delicious. What will I make next?" he says.

Did you enjoy this book?
Please leave a review.

SCAN ME

Auntie Sierra ™

CHILDREN'S BOOK AUTHOR | ENGINEER

STEM Education Advocate

www.AuntieSierra.com

Looking for at-home or classroom-related lessons?

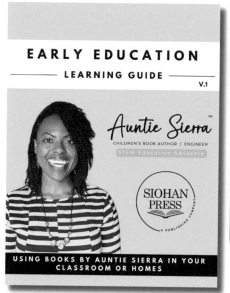

SCAN ME

Auntie Sierra ™

CHILDREN'S BOOK AUTHOR | ENGINEER

STEM Education Advocate

www.AuntieSierra.com

For an extended learning experience, grab the Coloring and Activity Book.

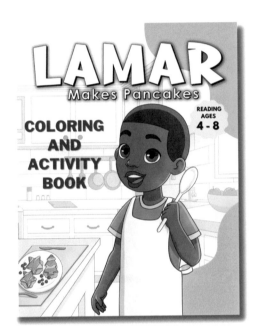

SCAN ME

Auntie Sierra ™

CHILDREN'S BOOK AUTHOR | ENGINEER

STEM Education Advocate

www.AuntieSierra.com

Made in the USA
Columbia, SC
07 October 2024